Granny

by Christine Dowe
illustrated by Dara Goldman

 HOUGHTON MIFFLIN   BOSTON

Printed in China

ISBN-13: 978-0-547-02689-3
ISBN-10: 0-547-02689-7

5 6 7 8 9 0940 15 14 13 12 11 10

Granny likes to sing.

fish

Granny likes to fish.

book

Granny likes to read.

paintbrush

Granny likes to paint.

bike

Granny likes to ride.

pool

Granny likes to swim.

game

Granny likes to play.

Granny likes to dance.

tree

Granny likes to sleep.

Responding

✔ **TARGET SKILL** **Understanding Characters** What does Granny like to do? What do these things show about Granny? Make a chart.

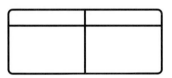

✏ Talk About It

Text to Text Think of a different story about a granny. What does she like to do?

WORDS TO KNOW

for	look
have	too
he	what

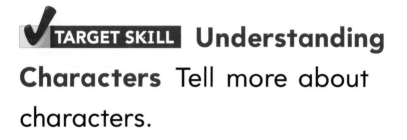

TARGET SKILL **Understanding Characters** Tell more about characters.

TARGET STRATEGY **Infer/Predict** Use clues to figure out more about story parts.

GENRE **Realistic fiction** is a story that could happen in real life.